MW00561877

# LED ZEPPELIN

# CONTENTS

# MUSICAL DEFINITIONS
## Terms used in this book

♩ = 120    This equation gives the definite tempo of the song and indicates that the speed of the note given in the equation is at that rate to a minute (i.e. 120 quarter notes are played in 1 minute).

Grace Notes - Undersized notes without computative value in the measure. The grace notes are to be played as close to the principle note as possible. The above applies to flams as well.

Placed in the staff is an indefinite symbol of measures "rested." A number placed within or above the staff indicates the number of measures to be rested.

Repeat the preceding measure in its entirety.

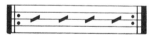

Repeat the measures within the repeat marks.

Repeat the preceding two measures in their entirety.

Play 1st ending, go back to repeat marks, then play through to 2nd ending. There can be an infinite number of endings.

⌢    Fermata - placed under or over a note or rest, hold the note at pleasure.

&gt;    Accent - When a note is given special emphasis.

Rolls are notated in this manner and are usually played as sixteenth note triplets or thirty-second notes, depending on the tempo. The note tied to the roll is to be played.

# NOTES & RESTS

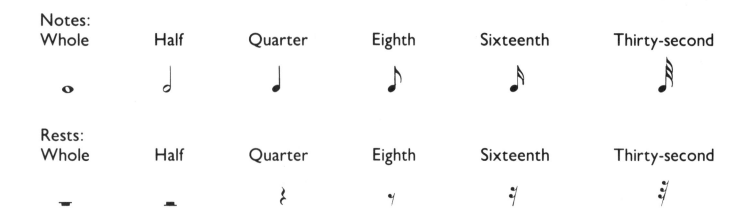

Notes:
Whole     Half     Quarter     Eighth     Sixteenth     Thirty-second

Rests:
Whole     Half     Quarter     Eighth     Sixteenth     Thirty-second

## Relative Value of Notes

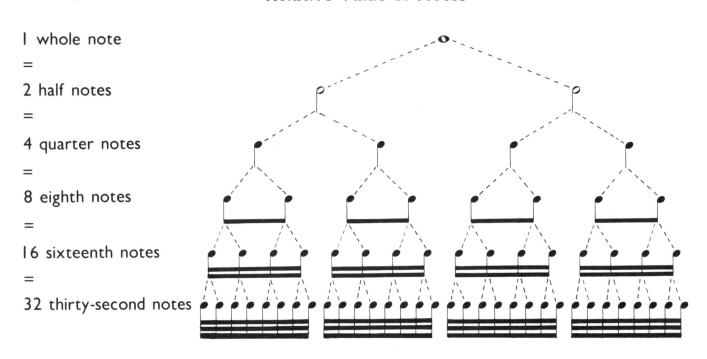

1 whole note

=

2 half notes

=

4 quarter notes

=

8 eighth notes

=

16 sixteenth notes

=

32 thirty-second notes

## Dotted notes & Rests

Single dot

=

Single dot

=

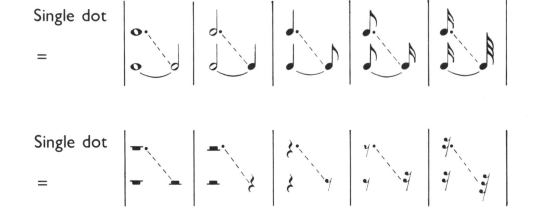

# ARTIFICIAL NOTES

## Eighth Note Triplets

Two eighth notes are equal to one quarter note. Three eighth notes can also equal a quarter note as long as there is a "3" above or below the three eighth notes. This is an eighth note triplet.

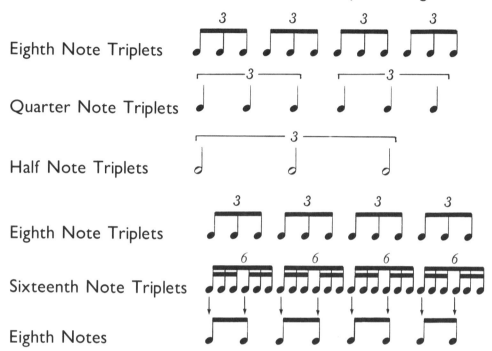

We will also see quarter note triplets and sixteenth note triplets. The examples below show the subdivision of triplets. Note the rhythmic alignment of the notes.

Eighth Note Triplets

Quarter Note Triplets

Half Note Triplets

Eighth Note Triplets

Sixteenth Note Triplets

Eighth Notes

# WAYS OF COUNTING

There are many ways to count rhythms. Several are shown below:

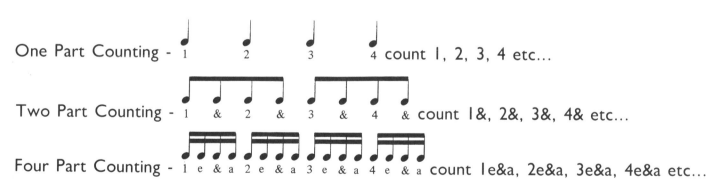

One Part Counting - 1  2  3  4 count 1, 2, 3, 4 etc...

Two Part Counting - 1 & 2 & 3 & 4 & count 1&, 2&, 3&, 4& etc...

Four Part Counting - 1 e & a 2 e & a 3 e & a 4 e & a count 1e&a, 2e&a, 3e&a, 4e&a etc...

## Triplet Counting -

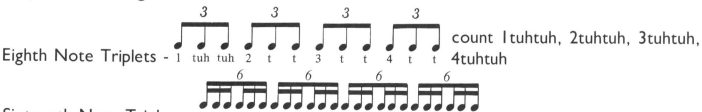

Eighth Note Triplets - 1 tuh tuh 2 t t 3 t t 4 t t count 1tuhtuh, 2tuhtuh, 3tuhtuh, 4tuhtuh

Sixteenth Note Triplets - 1 t t & t t 2 t t & t t 3 t t & t t 4 t t & t t count 1tuhtuh&tuhtuh, etc...

# TIME SIGNATURES

The time (or tempo) in which the song is to be played is indicated by two numerals placed at the beginning. This is called the time signature. The upper numeral tells us the number of beats to be played in a measure. The lower numeral tells us the note (or rest) that receives the beat. For example:

        4 = 4 beats to a measure.
        4 = The quarter note receives one beat.

        7 = 7 beats to a measure.
        8 = The eighth note receives one beat.

        7 = 7 beats to a measure.
     16 = The sixteenth note receives one beat.

        7 = 7 beats to a measure.
        4 = The quarter note receives one beat.

# DYNAMICS

Pianississimo - (ppp) very, very soft.

Pianissimo - (pp) very soft.

Piano - (p) soft.

MezzoPiano - (mp) moderately soft.

FortePiano - (fp) accent strongly, diminishing instantly to piano.

MezzoForte - (mf) moderately loud.

Forte - (f) loud.

Fortissimo - (ff) very loud.

Fortississimo - (fff) very, very loud.

     Crescendo - gradually louder.

     Decrescendo - gradually softer.

Ritard - gradually slower.

# DRUM LEGEND

The fifth line on the staff represents any cymbal or percussion instrument and is designated by its symbol or full name.

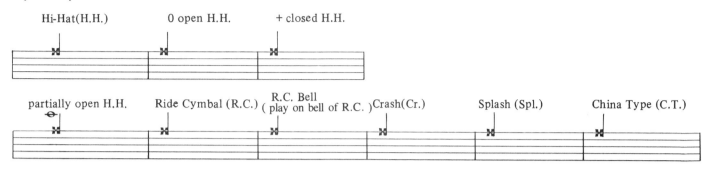

The first space above the staff, fifth line, fourth space and fourth line on the staff represent the 6", 8", 10" and 12" concert toms.

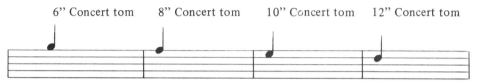

The third space on the staff represents the snare drum, timbales, cowbell and temple block.

*If more than one bell or block is being used they will be shown on the other lines or spaces according to the pitch of the instruments.

The third line, second space and second line represent the 12", 13" and 15" rack toms.

The first space on the staff represents the 18" floor tom.

The first line on the staff represents the bass drum(s)* and H.H. with foot.

*When the right and left bass drums are being used together they will be notated with a right (R) or a left (L).

Other Symbols:
Choke - quickly stop cymbal ringing by using your hand.
—————➤ Continue playing unless otherwise notated.

# DAZED AND CONFUSED

Words and Music by
JIMMY PAGE

# BLACK DOG

Words and Music by
JIMMY PAGE, ROBERT PLANT
and JOHN PAUL JONES

# D'YER MAK'ER

Words and Music by
JOHN BONHAM, JOHN PAUL JONES
and ROBERT PLANT

# WHOLE LOTTA LOVE

Words and Music by
JIMMY PAGE, ROBERT PLANT,
JOHN PAUL JONES and JOHN BONHAM

# GOOD TIMES BAD TIMES

Words and Music by
JIMMY PAGE, JOHN PAUL JONES
JOHN BONHAM, and ROBERT PLANT

# HEARTBREAKER

Words and Music by
JIMMY PAGE, ROBERT PLANT,
JOHN PAUL JONES and JOHN BONHAM

# IMMIGRANT SONG

Words and Music by
JIMMY PAGE and ROBERT PLANT

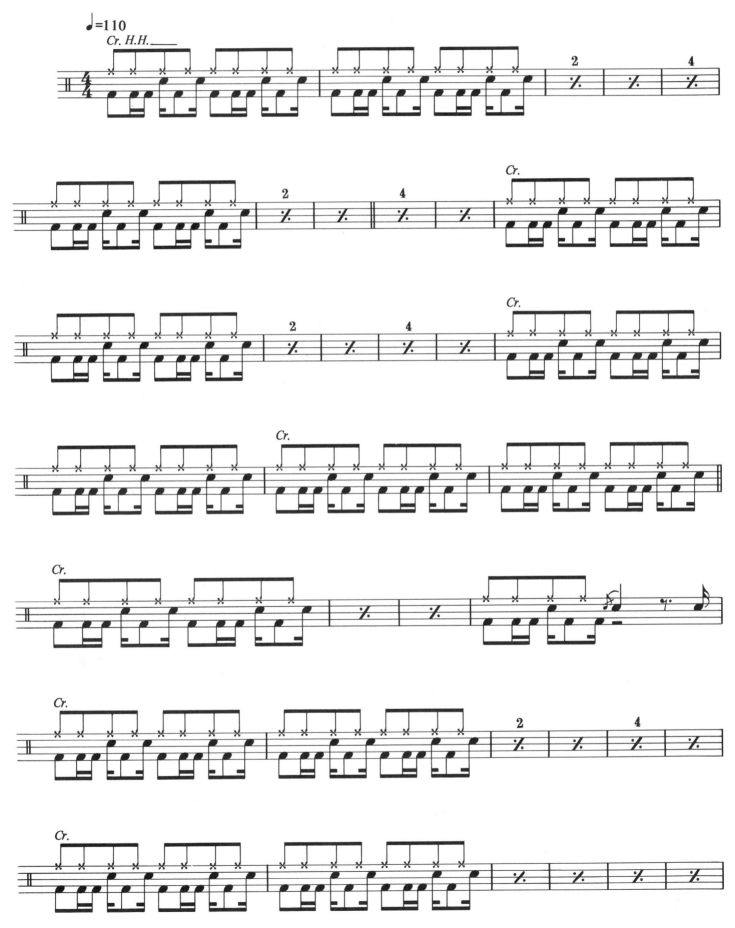

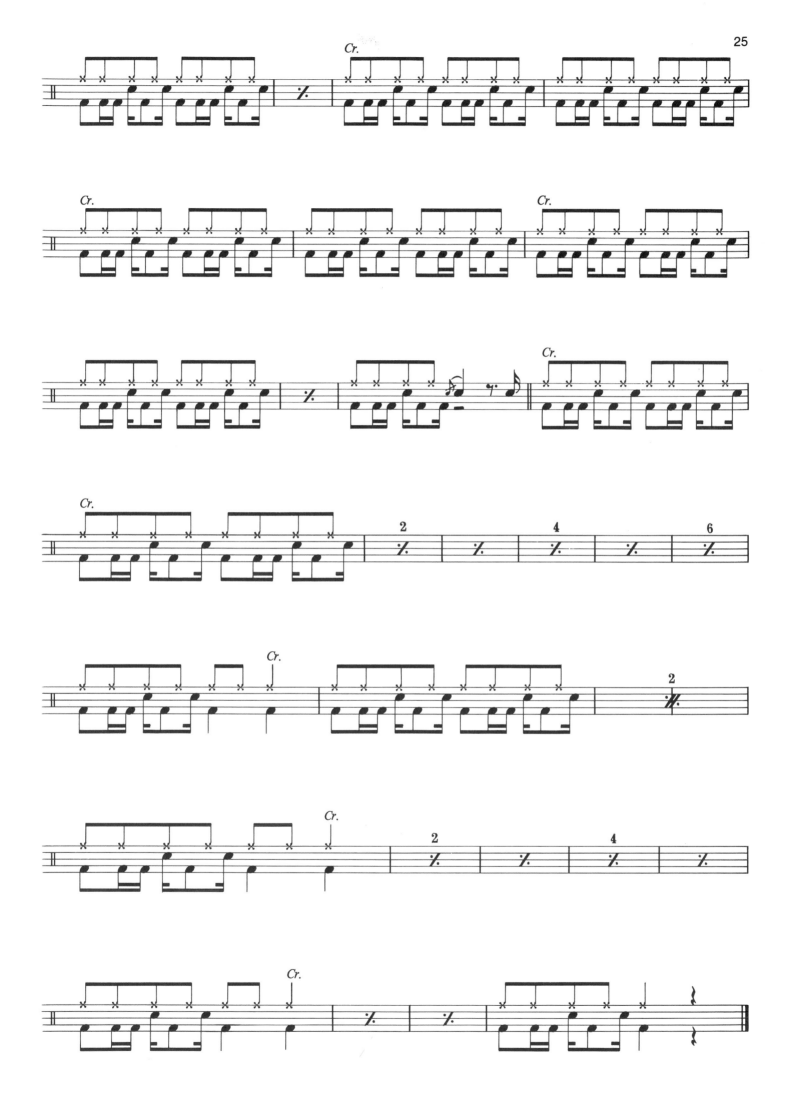

# THE OCEAN

Words and Music by
JOHN BONHAM, JOHN PAUL JONES,
JIMMY PAGE and ROBERT PLANT

# WHAT IS AND WHAT SHOULD NEVER BE

Words and Music by
JIMMY PAGE and ROBERT PLANT

30

# STAIRWAY TO HEAVEN

Words and Music by
JIMMY PAGE and ROBERT PLANT

© 1972, 1986 SUPERHYPE PUBLISHING
All rights administered by WB MUSIC CORP.
All Rights Reserved

And she's buying a stairway to heaven

ritard.